THE BEST OF
MATT
2011

'Have you finished
with the Government's
wellbeing survey?'

MATTHEW PRITCHETT
studied at St Martin's School of Art in London and first saw himself published in the *New Statesman* during one of its rare lapses from high seriousness. He has been the *Daily Telegraph*'s front-page pocket cartoonist since 1988. In 1995, 1996, 1999, 2005 and 2009 he was the winner of the Cartoon Arts Trust Award and in 1991, 2004 and 2006 he was 'What the Papers Say' Cartoonist of the Year. In 1996, 1998, 2000, 2008 and 2009 he was the *UK Press Gazette* Cartoonist of the Year and in 2002 he received an MBE.

Own your favourite Matt cartoons. Browse the full range of Matt cartoons and buy online at www.telegraph.co.uk/photographs or call 020 7931 2076.

'He's counting down to
the end of the Olympics'

The Daily Telegraph

THE BEST OF

MATT

2011

An Orion paperback

First published in Great Britain in 2011
by Orion Books
A division of the Orion Publishing Group Ltd
Orion House
5 Upper St Martin's Lane
London WC2H 9EA

An Hachette UK company

10 9 8 7 6 5 4 3 2 1

A CIP catalogue record for this book
is available from the British Library

ISBN 978 1 4091 2017 9

Printed in the UK by CPI William Clowes, Beccles NR34 7TL

The Orion Publishing Group's policy is to use papers that
are natural, renewable and recyclable products and
made from wood grown in sustainable forests. The logging
and manufacturing processes are expected to conform to
the environmental regulations of the country of origin.

www.orionbooks.co.uk

THE BEST OF
MATT
2011

I picked this one – about the French ban on the wearing of burkas – because I managed to do two things in it that I would not have thought possible in a pocket cartoon. First, I came up with a joke about Muslims and religious freedom, and secondly, I got six topless women onto the front page of the *Daily Telegraph*. The icing on the cake was that nobody issued a fatwa and I wasn't fired.

'I suppose I'll have
to buy a hat'

'April 29th – is that date
a bit too middle class?'

Couple name the day

'I'd no idea the Second World War was over, but I've heard all about the royal wedding'

'I plan to watch the wedding in the pub. I'm going for one last dress rehearsal'

'I knew I shouldn't have
married a commoner'

'Here come the Beckhams!'

That hat auctioned for charity

...and Bin Laden found

'This isn't what I expected
journalism college
to be like'

'Just fetch the newspaper.
Spare me the moralising'

'I've decided these will be the last chips to be wrapped in the News of the World'

'Now the paper boy has been arrested'

Paper closes and more arrests

'I'm the only one in the
Met with no links to
News International'

'I liked the pie throwing, but I thought the rest of it was disgraceful'

Rupert attacked at Select Committee

'News Corp ruled the world for many years. Nobody knows what wiped it out'

'I've been on holiday for a fortnight. Have I missed anything?'

The Phone Hacking Scandal

M.O.D. cuts

'After the RAF cuts he tried to do a victory roll'

'Ready, aim, FIRE!'

'I know you're in here
hiding from the
defence cuts'

'A new Trident missile?
You haven't used the old
one we bought for you!'

M.O.D. cuts

Cuts continue as wars increase

Sharing with the French

'Rule Britannia has been
cancelled due to the
defence cuts'

'I've ordered you a biscuit.
It will cost £1.1m and be
ready in 2014'

'Would you like me to
cut more slowly?'

'For better or worse?
You mean things could get
worse than they are now?'

Era of Austerity

'We're all in this together'

'I sent him to civil disobedience classes'

'The cuts have ruined the council fireworks display'

Era of Austerity

ECONOMIST ON HOLIDAY

'I went for a dip this
morning. A double dip is
now a possibility'

AINTREE

'Do we have a Plan B?'

'We're first time buyers and
the Government helped us
get this pothole'

'Drink driving. If you
don't mind me asking,
how do you afford it?'

Dear Granny,
Thanks for the gift voucher.
Due to the VAT increase you
will need to send me some
more money.

The Irish bail out

'I see you got a
100th birthday message
from the Queen'

'He's nine. In French years
he's already retired'

Benefits

'You could direct traffic'

'We wait for people to be
miraculously healed, then
we take away their benefits'

'After knocking the Health Secretary to the floor, put your hands round his throat...'

'I assure you I'm doing everything I can to save my budget'

'I can't remember if these are my budget figures or your cholesterol reading'

'I taught you to fetch,
to sit and to stay.
You owe me £9,000'

'I was awake all day
worrying about it'

'Well, this nails the myth that students do nothing but get drunk'

'Is this riot your own work or did you plagiarise one you found on the internet?'

'I'd love to throw barricades at the police, but my A-level grades weren't good enough'

'I hit a policeman, who hit a protester, who hit the Prince of Wales' car'

Prisoners' Votes

'I'm not voting.
After the expenses scandal
I think they're all as
bad as each other'

'A candidate's coming to the
door. Let's pretend we're out'

'A longer sentence?
But I have to get home
for the babysitter'

'If this is forest privatisation,
I'm all in favour'

'The Government has scaled
down the forest sell-off'

Labour Leadership

'Say what you like about the Krays, but they'd never have fought each other for the Labour leadership'

'Instead of the Red Flag, we'll be singing the Rolf Harris hit, Two Little Boys'

'As you can see, I picked
the wrong brother'

'I might consider voting
Labour, but I'd never go to a
Miliband family gathering'

'One advantage of having six
wives is that I can spread my
speeding points between them'

'I'm leaving you for a
woman with fewer points
on her licence'

'Now you're 18, I should tell you the gardener's really your father. It might help with your Oxbridge application'

'Don't tell Nick Clegg, but my father got me this job'

'We've been kettled
by snowmen'

'I'm sick of turkey. We're
having penguin this year'

'The 7.41 is cancelled because the driver is working from home'

'Will you be staying with us for just the one night?'

Weather

'Hello, darling, I made it to
work ... I'm going to
come home now'

'I can't see what's in your
eye, but we know it's not grit'

'You're old enough to be
told that the 11.32
doesn't really exist'

'You must come
to us next year'

Snow disrupts Christmas travel

'It's a miracle! The Pope's
luggage has arrived
with him'

'Two choc ices
and a 99, please'

'I can't tell you about the
birds and the bees — they've
obtained a super-injunction'

'I can hear the names of all
the celebrities with
super-injunctions'

'Now, can you get us a super-injunction?'

'Another super-injunction?'

'This rose is called Ryan Giggs, but don't tell anyone I told you'

Super-injunctions

'Not here. Not in front of the bonus'

'You have been charged £35. You're not allowed to ask why'

Sir Fred Goodwin

'A spot betting syndicate
has paid me £150,000 to
make a Victoria sponge'

'It's my husband's birthday,
so I'd like to pay for
England to win'

'In the summer the boys do
match fixing and in the
winter they do corruption
and vote selling'

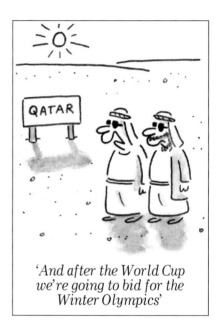

'And after the World Cup
we're going to bid for the
Winter Olympics'

'In many ways we were lucky
to get all the Olympic
tickets we applied for'

'I applied for Olympic tickets
and they offered me a place to
read geography at Sheffield'

'Is your husband in? I want
to ask him if Johnny can
come out and play'

'I'd like to apply for a job'

'Tasteless? That man likes it and those steaks are identical clones'

'Does that milk smell cloned to you?'

Arab Spring

'I was hoping for a more orderly transition of the remote control'

Arab Spring

LATEST GADDAFI RANT

'And, by the way, I hated
The King's Speech'

'I've just realised our house
looks like Colonel Gaddafi'

'When I joined this book club I thought we'd be discussing literature'

'Firelighters, petrol, matches ... right, I'm off to church'

'Warning: the following item
contains images that some
viewers may find magnificent'

'We had a disastrous holiday
in Italy. The whole country
is sniggering about
Cameron's Big Society'

Chilean Miners

'Right, I must go home,
my wife thinks I'm stuck
down a mine in Chile'

'If we stay underground for
69 days we'll miss the
spending review'

'If you won't be a
worker bee, I'll find you
some community work'

'I sponsor the child of a
higher rate taxpayer
in the UK'

And finally...

And finally...

'If we switch them into
reverse we can blow the
volcanic ash back to Iceland'

'I always think divorce is
particularly sad when
tattoos are involved'

'Before we conclude this all-day discussion, maybe we should mention finance'

Dominique Strauss-Kahn resigns

And finally...

'It's Shane Warne's
latest score'

'My son's in the Nativity
play – he's Bethlehem'

'Shame is forcing us to move. The neighbours discovered we only have the old iPad'

'Was I ever married to her?'

And finally...

And finally...

'Darling, is that the latest from Galliano?'

*'Wife brings you tea.
Coming up later: a biscuit?'*

*'This is a special occasion,
open a can of the 38p lager'*

Local news to be extended

And finally...

'I can't decide whether to mow
the lawn or set light to it'

Drought

'If I said this milk
was off, would it be
considered ageism?'

'Higher taxes and lower
wages – that's an
unfortunate combination'

'We got two tickets to watch
them dismantle the winners'
podium when it's all over'

And finally...

'Strikes have closed schools,
forcing many parents to take
their children to work'

'Can you make me look six
years older? I want to retire'

'The BBC has sent us a bill for our TV licence and a leaflet on assisted suicide'

'I don't know when I'll be back. I want you to try to forget me'

And finally...

'I propose that one of us should attempt to actually talk to a girl'

'That's the riskier side of the bank'